OUTBACK SCHOOL

Australian Map - Schools of the Air

Source: www.cultureandrecreation.gov.au dated 21 December 2007

OUTBACK SCHOOL

NORAH KERSH, CORRENA LUCAS & NICKY COOPER
ILLUSTRATED BY NORAH KERSH

National Library of Australia Cataloguing-in-Publication entry

Author: Lucas, Coreena.

Title: Outback school / Coreena Lucas & Nicky Cooper ; illustrated by Norah Kersh.

ISBN: 9781921555374 (pbk.)

Target Audience: For children.

Other Authors/Contributors: Cooper, Nicky.
Kersh, Norah.

Dewey Number: A823.4

Images: Courtesy of Education Queensland

Published by Boolarong Press, 1/655 Toohey Road, Salisbury, Queensland, Australia 4107

Typeset, printed and bound by Watson Ferguson & Company, Salisbury, Queensland, Australia 4107

Dedication

This book is dedicated to all the mums, dads and School of the Air teachers who have had such a positive impact on so many young lives through their commitment to learning in sometimes very difficult circumstances.

Dusty and Amy live on "Noonbah" cattle station. It's a long way from town.

"Dusty, Amy" Mum calls, "It is school time." Mum is their home tutor.

The children are feeding the poddy calves, Jazz and Starshine. "What a little greedy guts," scolds Amy, as her calf Jazz finishes her milk and pushes Starshine out of the way.

The children wash their hands and come into the school room on the end of the veranda. Dusty is in year 5, Amy in year 2. They each have their own desks, and on the table in the corner is the computer which they share.

“Oh! Oh!” baby sister Rosie has found the box of blocks and paints and has scattered them everywhere.

E
A
B

Dusty writes out his spelling list as Mum explains a maths problem to Amy.

What is that hum in the distance? Just then Dad sings out, “Who wants to meet the mail plane?” It is mail day and Mum lets the children go for a break.

wall
ATLAS
ATLAS
ATLAS
LANGUAGE
OTHER
THAN
ENGLISH

In a cloud of dust the 4-wheel drive arrives at the airstrip as the plane taxis to a stop. The pilot hands Dad the engine part that he has been waiting for. The children collect their school papers in separate bags. Amy can’t wait to see her new library books.

MAIL

It is time for Dusty's lesson over the internet with his SOTA teacher and classmates. Miss Hampton calls "Good Morning" to each of the children. First they share their news. Joe from Christmas Station with its big river and wild hills, tells of the road trains which left this morning loaded with steers on their way to Darwin. The cattle will board a ship to Indonesia.

Meg’s family are mustering contractors. She does school from a caravan among the gidgee trees. Her news is about Min her cattle dog which has six new pups.

Bernie, on the edge of the desert at Mt. Tommerhawk, was out checking the bores yesterday. He and his brother found that the windmill at O'Toole's Bore had been blown into a twisted mess by a whirlwind. Lucky they found this. A big repair job is needed so the cattle can have water.

Everyone in the class has news before the lesson begins. Dusty has to give a talk about Scott of the Antarctic. This unit is all about the Antarctic.

School is over for the day. Mum makes a cup of tea. Dusty and Amy race over to the stockyards where Jack, their older brother, is handling a young horse. Dust Devil dances around as Jack swings into the saddle. He stands stock still for a minute, then tosses his head and bucks all over the round yard, sweating and kicking up dust.

“Steady boy,” says Jack calmly. Before long Dust Devil is trotting about like an old stock horse.

That night around the dinner table, the family discuss what will happen the next day. Cluster Muster will start on Wednesday.

From all parts of the outback, School of the Air families will travel to the school for a get-together. Some of the children have not met in person, but know each other from the voices “on air.”

Dad has fuelled the car up. He put in an extra spare tyre and fan belt. Mum has packed the tucker box and baby things, Dusty and Amy have swags ready and water containers filled.

Before sun-up they are on their way.

The track is red and sandy. Spinifex are scattered across the country like big pincushions.

Mirage shimmers in the distance as the day grows hotter. Now they see a blue range ahead. Through a rocky gap they stop for sandwiches from the tucker box. A rock-hole here has lovely water for the children to paddle. Rosie sits in the water laughing and splashing.

Refreshed, they set off on the last leg of their trip.

Who will they meet tomorrow?

Teachers greet the children and do some school work together. What a novelty. Next a tour showing how School of the Air was before the internet. The old radio room is now a museum.

Then, sports! Sack-races, 3 legged races, egg-in-spoon races. A lot of fun.

As the stars come out Dusty and Amy chat with their friends and share almost burnt sausages. Mum and Dad are doing the same.

It was a great day.

School of the Air - Then and Now

The Reverend John Flynn established the Royal Flying Doctor Service (RFDS) after recognising that there was an urgent need for medical and health care to people living in remote communities. Alfred Traegar invented the pedal-powered radio which allowed remote Australians to contact the Flying Doctor.

In 1946, Miss Adelaide Miethke was vice-President of the South Australian branch of the RFDS and was a former inspector of girl's schools. The School of the Air (SOA) was born when she noticed how outback children were taught to use the radio network. Children living in remote areas had to attend boarding school or receive their lessons by mail. There was no interaction with teachers and other students.

In 1948 the Alice Springs RFDS base was used to broadcast the first school lesson to outback children. The SOA was established a few years later and it quickly spread to the other states and territories. The SOA was made famous in the late 1960s when it was featured on *Skippy The Bush Kangaroo*.

In 2005 there were more than 16 schools covering 1.5 million square kilomotres. The program now extends to secondary and adult education. The SOA has helped many other countries where families and education services are separated by large distances.

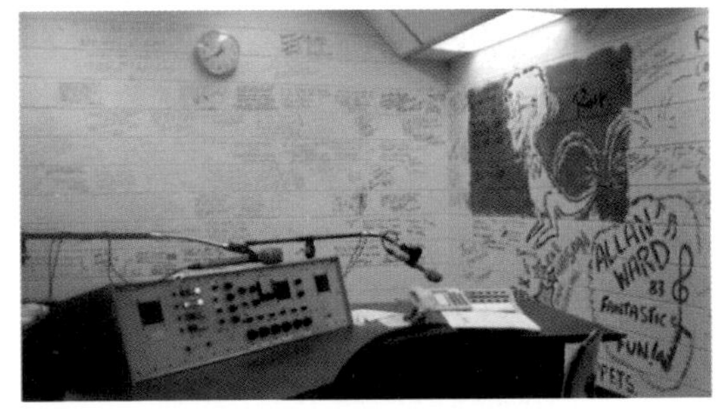

School of the Air, Alice Springs

Other publications available from www.boolarongpress.com.au:
Traegar The Pedal Radio Man Fred McKay
Outback Achiever Fred McKay

Left: *In 1928, Alfred Traegar put on his Sunday suit to show his boss, Flynn of the Inland, what the miracle pedal wireless machine really looked like.*

Right: *The first installation at Augustus Downs on June 19, 1929 operated by Mrs Gertrude Rothery.*

Source: Traegar The Pedal Radio Man, Fred McKay

On the air while reviewing her work.

Source: School of the Air, Mt Isa

Jack Cause's family are contract yard builders all over the north-west. Here he is having a lesson via satellite phone with his Year 7 teacher, Mr Cooper.

Source: School of the Air, Mt Isa

The internet is used extensively today.

Source: School of the Air, Mt Isa

Norah Kersh, well-respected writer and illustrator of outback children's books and winner of the May Gibbs Fellow, always dreamed of becoming a writer but it wasn't till the death of her grandson that she decided to take her dream seriously.

While helping her children to read and write, Norah often wished there were books that spoke of the outback-Australian experience. The stories her children read were about things that they didn't relate to or understand. The stories were about city kids who wore shoes and socks and welcomed their father home after a long day at the office. She wanted to have stories to which outback children could relate. Stories about cattle dogs, sheep, cows, wet seasons and dry seasons.